Picture Level

Specific Skill Series

Detecting the Sequence

Richard A. Boning

Fifth Edition

SRA/McGraw-Hill

Columbus, Ohio

Cover, Back Cover, Wayne Lynch/Masterfile

SRA/McGraw-Hill

A Division of The McGraw·Hill Companies

Printed in the United States of America.

Send all inquiries to:
    SRA/McGraw-Hill
    250 Old Wilson Bridge Road, Suite 310
    Worthington, OH 43085

ISBN 0-02-687989-1

    4 5 6 7 8 9 IMP 00 99

To the Teacher

PURPOSE:
DETECTING THE SEQUENCE helps develop the important ability to determine time relationships—the order in which things happen. Proficiency in this often taken-for-granted skill is necessary in all kinds of academic and nonacademic reading, from narration to process explanation.

FOR WHOM:
The skill of DETECTING THE SEQUENCE is developed through a series of books spanning ten levels (Picture, Preparatory, A, B, C, D, E, F, G, H). The Picture Level is for pupils who have not acquired a basic sight vocabulary. The Preparatory Level is for pupils who have a basic sight vocabulary but are not yet ready for the first-grade-level book. Books A through H are appropriate for pupils who can read on levels one through eight, respectively. **The use of the *Specific Skill Series Placement Test* is recommended to determine the appropriate level.**

THE NEW EDITION:
DETECTING THE SEQUENCE has been designed to help improve students' skills in identifying the sequence of events within a reading selection. In this series, the variety of questions helps develop students' understanding of multiple ways of expressing time relationships. Questions are text-dependent rather than picture-dependent.

SESSIONS:
Short practice sessions are the most effective. It is desirable to have a practice session every day or every other day, using a few units each session.

To the Teacher

SCORING:

Pupils should record their answers on the reproducible worksheets. The worksheets make scoring easier and provide uniform records of the pupils' work. Using worksheets also avoids consuming the exercise books.

It is important for pupils to know how well they are doing. For this reason, units should be scored as soon as they have been completed. Then a discussion can be held in which pupils justify their choices. (The Integrated Language Activities, many of which are open-ended, do not lend themselves to an objective score; thus there are no answer keys for these pages.)

GENERAL INFORMATION ON *DETECTING THE SEQUENCE*:

DETECTING THE SEQUENCE helps develop sequence skills through three general types of questions: (1) those that focus directly on when an event happened; (2) those that focus on which of several events happened first (or last) among the events mentioned; and (3) those that focus on whether a particular event happened before, at the same time as, or after another. The teacher should make clear to students that a question reading "Which happened first (last)?" means "Which happened before (after) any of the *other answer choices*?" (not "Which happened first [last] in the entire reading selection?").

Answering questions in DETECTING THE SEQUENCE involves more than just reading for facts. Most questions require pupils to establish the time relationships between two separately stated ideas by utilizing time clues in the text. (On the Picture Level, pupils examine two pictures illustrating a sequence of events, and determine which event happened first.)

SUGGESTED STEPS:

On all levels above Picture, pupils should read each story carefully. At the end of each statement they should try to form a picture in their minds so that they will clearly understand what happened first, second, and so forth. As they read, pupils should look for key words that serve as sequence clues, such as *then, before, soon, finally, later, while, when,* and *now.* After finishing the story, pupils should review it mentally. Without looking at the story, they should be able to recall the sequence in which events occurred. If they cannot do this, they should reread the story. Pupils should then answer the questions on their worksheets. In answering, pupils may look at the story as often as necessary.

RELATED MATERIALS:

Specific Skill Series Placement Tests, which enable the teacher to place pupils at their appropriate levels in each skill, are available for the Elementary (Pre-1–6) and Midway (4–8) grade levels.

In real life, things happen in a certain order. First one thing happens, then another. When you hear a story it is usually told in order, too. Things that happened first are told first.

Can you tell the order in which things happened in these sentences?

Jan put on her hat. Then she went out.

Which happened first: *Jan went out* or *Jan put on her hat*? You can tell that Jan put on her hat first. The word *then* tells you.

Often one thing must happen before another thing can happen. You must get on your bike before you can ride it. You can't read a book until after you have opened it. You know what happens first because it would not make sense for things to happen the other way around.

In this book, you will look at pictures that go together. One of the pictures has an **A** under it and one has a **B** under it. Look at what is happening in each picture. Then answer the question, "What happened first?" Write **A** on your answer sheet if picture A shows what happened first. Write **B** if picture B shows what happened first.

PICTURE A

What happened first?

PICTURE **B**

picture **A**   or   picture **B**

PICTURE **A**

What happened first?

PICTURE **B**

picture **A**   or   picture **B**

PICTURE A

What happened first?

PICTURE **B**

picture **A**   or   picture **B**

PICTURE **A**

What happened first?

PICTURE **B**

picture **A**   or   picture **B**

PICTURE A

What happened first?

PICTURE **B**

picture **A**   or   picture **B**

PICTURE A

What happened first?

PICTURE **B**

picture **A**   or   picture **B**

A. Exercising Your Skill

This girl must get ready for school. What will she do **first**:

1. wake up or brush her hair?
2. put on her shoes or put on her socks?
3. eat breakfast or catch the bus?

B. Expanding Your Skill

Play "When Do You...?" Take turns with a friend. Ask questions about getting ready for school. Begin each question with "When do you...?" Use the word *before* or *after* to answer.

("When do you brush your teeth?" "I brush my teeth **after** I have breakfast.")

C. Exploring Language

Tell what number or letter comes next.

B   C   D   —

3   4   5   —

6   7   8   —

R   S   T   —

W   X   Y   —

D. Expressing Yourself

Do one of these things.

1. Draw four pictures of things you do to get ready for school. Draw them in order. Number them in order.

2. Act out four things you do before you come to school. Act them out in order. Ask your classmates to guess what you are doing.

PICTURE **A**

What happened first?

PICTURE **B**

picture **A**   or   picture **B**

PICTURE A

What happened first?

PICTURE **B**

picture **A**   or   picture **B**

PICTURE A

What happened first?

PICTURE **B**

picture **A**   or   picture **B**

PICTURE A

What happened first?

PICTURE **B**

picture **A**   or   picture **B**

PICTURE **A**

What happened first?

PICTURE **B**

picture **A**   or   picture **B**

PICTURE A

What happened first?

PICTURE B

picture **A** or picture **B**

A. Exercising Your Skill

Let's pretend you are going to plant a flower in a pot. Tell which thing to do **first**.

- Make a hole in the dirt with your finger.
- Put the seed in the hole.
- Fill a flower pot with dirt.
- Cover the seed with dirt.

B. Expanding Your Skill

Draw four steps in growing a plant. It can be a flower or a vegetable. Show how the plant grows and changes.

Put your pictures on separate sheets of paper. Mix up the pictures. See if a friend can number the pictures in order.

C. Exploring Language

Listen to the "True Plant Stories." Tell what comes first, next, and last in each story.

I AM A PUMPKIN.

My seed puts out a little green plant.

I grow leaves and a big orange fruit.

People carve me into a smiling face.

I AM STRAW.

People pick me and dry me.

I grow in a big field.

I am tied together to sweep a room.

I AM CATNIP.

I make your cat happy.

People put me inside cat toys.

I grow green and thick.

D. Expressing Yourself

Pick a plant you would like to be. It can be a flower, a tree, or a vegetable. Tell your life story and act it out for the class. Begin when you are a seed.

PICTURE A

What happened first?

PICTURE **B**

picture **A** or picture **B**

PICTURE **A**

What happened first?

PICTURE **B**

picture **A**   or   picture **B**

PICTURE A

What happened first?

PICTURE **B**

picture **A**   or   picture **B**

PICTURE A

What happened first?

PICTURE **B**

picture **A**   or   picture **B**

PICTURE A

What happened first?

PICTURE **B**

picture **A**   or   picture **B**

PICTURE A

What happened first?

PICTURE B

picture **A**   or   picture **B**

PICTURE A

What happened first?

PICTURE **B**

picture **A**   or   picture **B**

A. Exercising Your Skill

Babies learn many things. Tell which thing they learn **first**.

- to roll over or to walk?
- to run or to crawl?
- to drink from a cup or to drink from a bottle?
- to play patty-cake or baseball?

B. Expanding Your Skill

Look at the picture. This girl is walking with her balloon. What things did she learn to do **before** she learned how to walk? What can someone learn to do **after** learning to walk?

C. Exploring Language

Help put the blocks in order. Write them in ABC order on a sheet of paper.

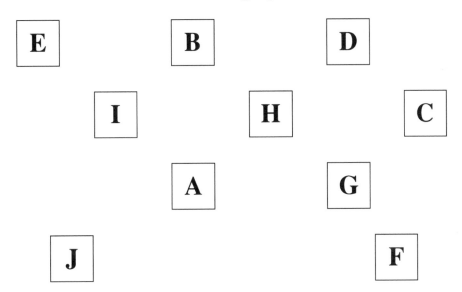

D. Expressing Yourself

Do one of these things.

1. Tell a story about a baby growing up. What things did the baby learn to do first? Second? Third?

2. List things you want to learn as you continue to grow up. Put them in order.

PICTURE A

What happened first?

PICTURE **B**

picture **A**   or   picture **B**

PICTURE A

What happened first?

UNIT 21

PICTURE B

picture **A**   or   picture **B**

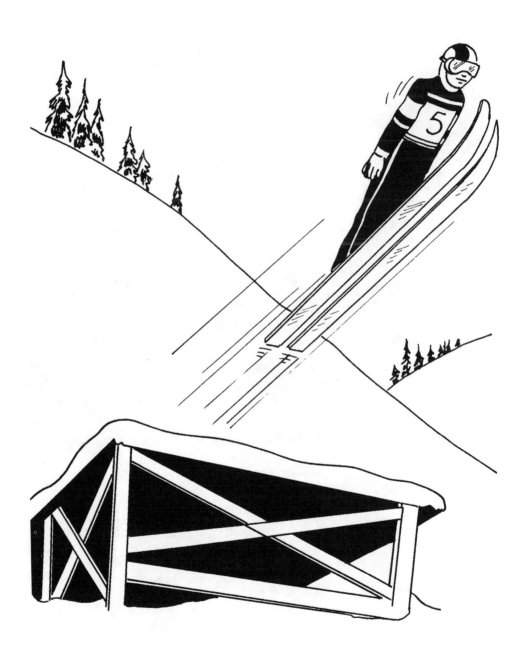

PICTURE **A**

What happened first?

PICTURE **B**

picture **A**   or   picture **B**

PICTURE A

What happened first?

PICTURE **B**

picture **A**   or   picture **B**

PICTURE A

What happened first?

PICTURE **B**

picture **A**   or   picture **B**

PICTURE **A**

What happened first?

PICTURE B

picture **A**   or   picture **B**

A. Exercising Your Skill

Tell how to do these jobs. What should you do first? Second? Third?

Dusting
- Put things back on the furniture.
- Take things off the furniture.
- Wipe the furniture with a cloth.

Washing Dishes
- Scrub the dishes.
- Rinse the soap off.
- Fill a pan with water and soap.

B. Expanding Your Skill

Think about a job you can do. Think of all the steps. Now act out the job for the class, step by step. Be sure to show things in order. See who can guess the job.

C. Exploring Language

Read the name of the job. Give three steps to follow to do the job. Make sure you give the steps in order.

Water the grass. _____
_____

Walk the dog. _____
_____

Set the table. _____
_____

D. Expressing Yourself

Do one of these things.

1. Tell the steps to do something. Do not tell what the something is. See how many steps you give before the class can guess what you are thinking of.

2. Get three different pieces of paper. On each piece of paper, draw a step that shows how to do a job. Mix up the papers. See if your classmates can put the pictures in order.